Friendly Neighborhood
SPIDER-MAN

Secrets and Rumors

Friendly Neighborhood SPIDER-MAN

Secrets and Rumors

Tom Taylor
Writer

Juann Cabal (#1-4 &#6) &
Yildiray Cinar (#5) with
Marcelo Ferreira (#1 backup)
Artists

Douglas Franchin (#4, pages 18-20) & **Roberto Poggi** (#1 backup)
Inkers

Nolan Woodard (#1-6) with
Federico Blee (#6) & **Jim Campbell** (#1 backup)
Color Artists

VC's Travis Lanham
Letterer

Andrew C. Robinson
Cover Artist

Kathleen Wisneski
Assistant Editor

Nick Lowe
Editor

Spider-Man created by **Stan Lee** & **Steve Ditko**

Collection Editor **Mark D. Beazley**
Assistant Editor **Caitlin O'Connell**
Associate Managing Editor **Kateri Woody**
Senior Editor, Special Projects **Jennifer Grünwald**
VP Production & Special Projects **Jeff Youngquist**
Book Designer **Adam Del Re**

SVP Print, Sales & Marketing **David Gabriel**
Director, Licensed Publishing **Sven Larson**
Editor in Chief **C.B. Cebulski**
Chief Creative Officer **Joe Quesada**
President **Dan Buckley**
Executive Producer **Alan Fine**

FRIENDLY NEIGHBORHOOD SPIDER-MAN VOL. 1: SECRETS AND RUMORS. Contains material originally published in magazine form as FRIENDLY NEIGHBORHOOD SPIDER-MAN #1-6. First printing 2019. ISBN 978-1-302-91690-9. Published by MARVEL WORLDWIDE, INC., a subsidiary of MARVEL ENTERTAINMENT, LLC. OFFICE OF PUBLICATION: 135 West 50th Street, New York, NY 10020. © 2019 MARVEL No similarity between any of the names, characters, persons, and/or institutions in this magazine with those of any living or dead person or institution is intended, and any such similarity which may exist is purely coincidental. **Printed in the U.S.A.** DAN BUCKLEY, President, Marvel Entertainment; JOHN NEE, Publisher; JOE QUESADA, Chief Creative Officer; TOM BREVOORT, SVP of Publishing; DAVID BOGART, Associate Publisher & SVP of Talent Affairs; DAVID GABRIEL, SVP of Sales & Marketing, Publishing; JEFF YOUNGQUIST, VP of Production & Special Projects; DAN CARR, Executive Director of Publishing Technology; ALEX MORALES, Director of Publishing Operations; DAN EDINGTON, Managing Editor; SUSAN CRESPI, Production Manager; STAN LEE, Chairman Emeritus. For information regarding advertising in Marvel Comics or on Marvel.com, please contact Vit DeBellis, Custom Solutions & Integrated Advertising Manager, at vdebellis@marvel.com. For Marvel subscription inquiries, please call 888-511-5480. **Manufactured between 5/17/2019 and 6/18/2019 by LSC COMMUNICATIONS INC., KENDALLVILLE, IN, USA**

10 9 8 7 6 5 4 3 2 1

Mother of Exiles: Part One

New York.
Liberty Island.

I KNOW WHAT IT'S LIKE TO BE SCARED.

TO BE PRACTICALLY FROZEN IN FEAR.

IN MY EARLY DAYS, STANDING ON TOP OF A BUILDING, GETTING READY TO JUMP OFF?

TRUSTING I WOULDN'T GO SPLAT BECAUSE OF SOME WEBFLUID I'D DESIGNED MYSELF AND SUPER-POWERS I'D JUST GOTTEN FROM A SPIDER?

THAT WAS...A LITTLE SCARY.

AGHHH!

BUT THEN, THERE'D BE A SCREAM. SOMETHING THAT NEEDED MY ATTENTION MORE THAN MY FEAR. SOMETHING MORE IMPORTANT THAN MY SAFETY.

AND SO, I'D JUMP.

IT'S WHAT I DO.

I'M PETER PARKER...

AND THIS IS MY NEIGHBORHOOD.

AGHHHH!

REALLY, IT WAS ONLY A MATTER OF TIME BEFORE THIS HAPPENED.

THE "TWO-DAY" POTHOLE REPAIR ON THE BRIDGE IS IN ITS THIRD MONTH.

THEY FOUND A PIPE ISSUE WHEN THEY WERE FIXING THE POTHOLE, THEN THEY FOUND A STRUCTURAL ISSUE, THEN THEY FOUND...YOU GET THE IDEA.

BEFORE THE BRIDGE, THERE ARE MULTIPLE LANES THAT HAVE BECOME A LABYRINTHINE MESS OF CONFUSING AND CONTRADICTORY SIGNS.

MERGE LEFT...BUT NOT AFTER 2 P.M.... OR IF YOU'RE A SAGITTARIUS.

IT'S OKAY, KID.

YOU'RE GOING TO BE--

AGHHH!!!

SQUISH!

SMCK

OH MY GOD.

THANK YOU!

UM... I'M SORRY JORDIE TRIED TO SQUISH YOU.

HERE.

IT'S ALL GOOD. TO BE FAIR, I DON'T EXACTLY HAVE THE MOST KID-FRIENDLY COSTUME. IT LITERALLY HAS A SPIDER ON IT.

PETER. I ALMOST THOUGHT YOU WEREN'T GOING TO SHOW.

I LIVE HERE, MARNIE. I WAS ALWAYS GOING TO SHOW.

BUT, YES, I REMEMBERED YOU'D BE DONE WITH YOUR SHOPPING BY TWELVE, AND I DON'T LIKE LETTING PEOPLE DOWN.

REALLY? AREN'T YOU A NATIONAL DISGRACE?*

YEAH. ON AND OFF.

*PETER RECENTLY LOST HIS JOB BECAUSE OF A PLAGIARISM CHARGE THAT IS...MOSTLY UNTRUE? CHECK OUT AMAZING SPIDER-MAN! --NICK

I KNOW I'VE SAID THIS BEFORE, BUT THE BUILDING HAS AN ELEVATOR.

I DON'T TRUST ELEVATORS.

DOES ONE OWE YOU MONEY OR...?

I HAD A LOVER STOLEN BY ONE.

OH. I'M SO SORRY.

I'M JUST KIDDING.

I'VE NEVER HAD A LOVER STOLEN. I'VE ALWAYS GIVEN THEM AWAY.

THEN...?

THEY'RE LOCKED ROOMS DANGLING FROM A CABLE IN THE AIR, PETER.

I DIDN'T GET TO BE MY AGE BY WILLINGLY CLIMBING INTO SUCH OBVIOUS DEATH TRAPS.

OKAY. HERE GOES.

KNOCK KNOCK

CNK
CNK
SHNK

HELLO?

YES?

SHE'S TERRIFIED.

UM...

I HAVE APPLES.

HI. LOOK, I'M JUST DOWN THE HALL. APARTMENT 75. AND...

YOU'RE PETER?

HUH?

YES?

I'M LEILANI. MARNIE... SHE SAID YOU KNOW A SUPER HERO?

SHE PLOTTED THIS. THAT ELEVATOR-HATER SET ME UP.

"...THAT'S VERY KIND."

PETE!

LOOK!

OH MAN. THAT'S A HECK OF A TIP.

LET US BUY YOU LUNCH.

NAH. IT'S OKAY, GRACIE. YOU ENJOY IT.

YOU HAVEN'T WALKED PAST US ONCE WITHOUT HELPING. YOU'VE GIVEN US SOMETHING EVERY DAMN DAY WITHOUT ANY JUDGMENT. WE GOT LUCKY AND WE'RE BUYING YOU LUNCH.

OKAY. SURE. WHERE ARE WE DINING?

ONLY THE BEST.

YOU GET THE PICK OF THE CART, MAN.

GARY. GIVE ME WHICHEVER ONE YOU'D STILL EAT.

UM... I MIGHT MAKE A FRESH BATCH.

THIS IS...IT'S NOT A LIFE-CHANGING AMOUNT OF CASH FOR ANYONE.

BUT IT'S TODAY-CHANGING, AND THAT'S SOMETHING.

A TRUCK CRASH AND A HOT DOG. IT'S BEEN A BIT QUIET LATELY.

I CAN'T HELP BUT NOTICE THE EVIL IN THIS IMMEDIATE AREA SEEMS...A LITTLE LIGHT? IT'S ALMOST AS IF SOMEONE ELSE IS WORKING MY PATCH. NOT THAT I'M COMPLAINING, OF COURSE. MUCH.

IT'S JUST...

SOMETHING'S WRONG.

SOMETHING'S VERY WRONG.

NO. NO. NO.

PETER...

JUST GET HER OUT OF THE ROOM. WORRY ABOUT THE NEXT BIT NEXT.

LEILANI. WHO'S THIS?

UM... HOT DOG DELIVERY.

WHY DOES SHE KNOW YOUR NAME?

GENERAL COURTESY?

YES. THANKS, SPIDEY-SENSE. I KNOW A PUNCH IS COMING.

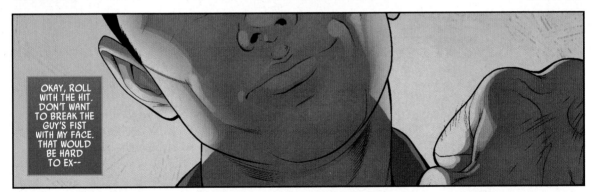

OKAY, ROLL WITH THE HIT. DON'T WANT TO BREAK THE GUY'S FIST WITH MY FACE. THAT WOULD BE HARD TO EX--

HOW LONG WAS I OUT?

WE FOUND YOU ABOUT HALF AN HOUR AGO. I CALLED THE POLICE AS SOON AS I GOT HERE.

THEY'RE NOT COMING.

CLEARLY, WHOEVER TOOK LEILANI IS JUST AS CONNECTED AS SHE SAID.

AND THIS WASN'T JUST ABOUT HER. THE APARTMENT'S TRASHED.

THEY WERE *LOOKING* FOR SOMETHING.

RANDY, CAN YOU STAY WITH MARNIE IN CASE THE COPS COME?

SURE.

THE COPS WON'T COME. I HAVE TO GET OUT THERE.

TAKE APPLES.

I...

...SURE.

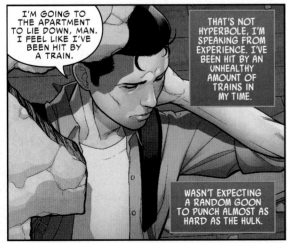

I'M GOING TO THE APARTMENT TO LIE DOWN, MAN. I FEEL LIKE I'VE BEEN HIT BY A TRAIN.

THAT'S NOT HYPERBOLE, I'M SPEAKING FROM EXPERIENCE. I'VE BEEN HIT BY AN UNHEALTHY AMOUNT OF TRAINS IN MY TIME.

WASN'T EXPECTING A RANDOM GOON TO PUNCH ALMOST AS HARD AS THE HULK.

OH NO. I FORGOT WHAT'S ON THE OTHER SIDE OF THE DOOR.

MY AND RANDY'S APARTMENT HAS BEEN INVADED...

GAH!

I KNOW WHAT IT'S LIKE TO BE SCARED.

TO BE PRACTICALLY FROZEN IN FEAR.

FROM THE FEAR OF KNOCKING ON A STRANGER'S DOOR...

...TO THE FEAR OF THE UNKNOWN...

OH, MAN.

...TO THE FEAR OF SUDDEN RESPONSIBILITY.

APPLES?

To Be Continued...

Mother of Exiles: Part Two

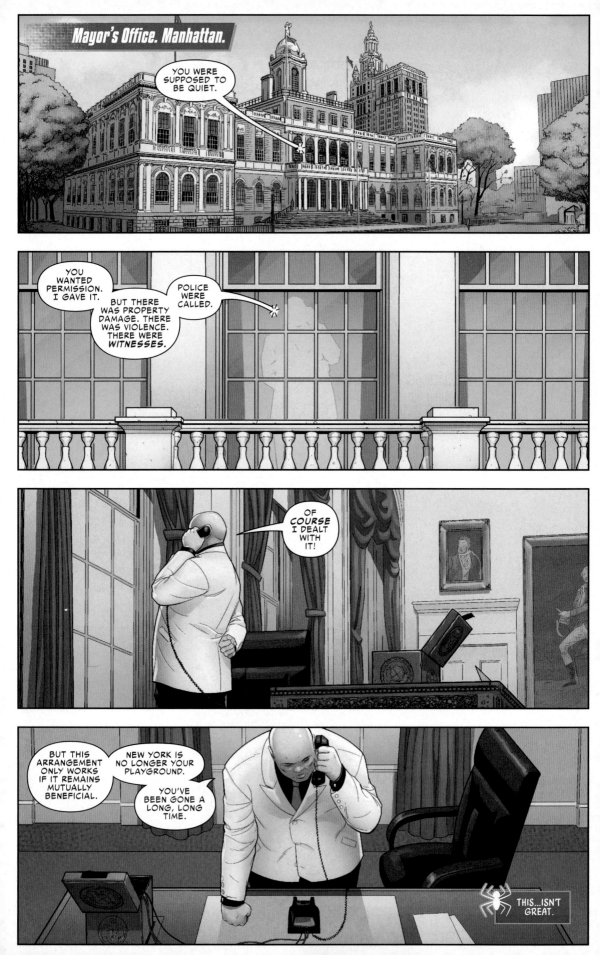

MOM LEFT US HERE. I DON'T KNOW WHERE SHE WENT.

HAS... HAS YOUR MOM EVER *LEFT* YOU?

UH... YEAH.

YEAH, SHE DID, ONCE.

TELL THEM WHAT THEY NEED TO HEAR, PETER.

YOUR MOM WILL BE BACK SOON.

BUT I'M GOING TO HAVE TO GO AND GET HER.

THEN WORK OUT HOW TO MAKE THAT A REALITY.

YOU'RE LEAVING US ALONE?

NO WAY.

I JUST NEED TO MAKE A CALL.

DEET

YEAH. HEY. I NEED A FAVOR. IT'S URGENT.

COULD YOU COME 'ROUND?

AND BE DISCREET.

THANKS.

dream of you

DING DONG

THAT'S TOO FAST. IT CAN'T BE HIM.

KIDS. I NEED YOU TO HIDE.

WE HAVE TO HIDE A LOT. WE'RE REALLY GOOD AT IT.

OKAY. QUICKLY...

"...THERE'S SOMEONE AT THE DOOR."

URGH.

WHO ARE YOU?

IS PETER HERE?

75

HE'S IN HIS ROOM.

SORRY, LADY. I WASN'T EXPECTING VISITORS. I'M SURE ALL THIS IS A LITTLE...

INADEQUATE. YES.

INADEQUATE...?

HELLO? IT'S MARNIE FROM APARTMENT 71.

I JUST WANTED TO LET YOU KNOW YOUR FRIEND, RANDY, IS STILL WAITING, BUT THE POLICE STILL HAVEN'T APPEARED.

A WOMAN DOWN THE HALL WAS TAKEN BY SOME SUPER-STRONG THUGS. SHE LEFT THE KIDS HERE BEFORE THEY TOOK HER.

SHE WANTED HELP.

I SAID I'D HELP HER, JOHNNY.

WHAT DO YOU NEED?

I NEED YOU TO LOOK AFTER THESE KIDS. KEEP THE DOOR LOCKED, STOP ANYONE FROM COMING IN, INCLUDING MY ROOMMATES, AND PRETEND TO BE ME.

OKAY. I'LL START PRACTICING TERRIBLE JOKES THAT POORLY MASK MY MANY INSECURITIES.

THANK YOU.

JOHNNY, THIS IS TIERRA AND JASPER.

HI!

JASPER DOESN'T SPEAK MUCH. AND THEY'RE NOT FROM AROUND HERE, SO THEY DON'T REALLY KNOW--

YOU'RE THE HUMAN TORCH!

I SURE AM.

WE KNOW ALL ABOUT YOU. YOU'RE AMAZING.

OUCH.

RIGHT. OKAY. I GUESS I'LL GO.

WHAT ARE YOU GOING TO DO?

I'M GOING TO START...

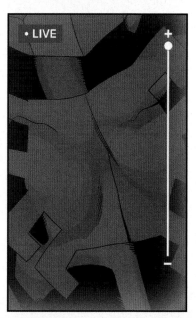

THD

HNF!

NO!

SCREEEEE

CAN'T LET HIM GET AWAY. I HAVE QUESTIONS!

THWIP

YES!

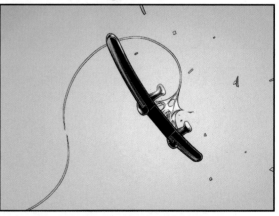

TNK

OKAY. LESS YES.

SPIDER-MAN?

YEAH?

YOU OKAY UNDER THERE?

SURE. IT'S NOT THE FIRST TIME I'VE HAD A LARGE CHUNK OF NEW YORK CRUSHING MY STERNUM, AND IT WON'T BE THE LAST.

I'M DETECTIVE SHARI SEBBENS.

NICE WORK HERE.

SERIOUSLY?

YES. YOU SAVED A LOT OF PEOPLE.

ARE YOU... NEW?

I AM. JUST STARTED AT THE PRECINCT THIS WEEK. WE WERE SUPPOSED TO BE MOVING IN EARLIER TODAY, BUT MY HUSBAND DROVE OUR MOVING TRUCK OFF A BRIDGE.

OH.

OH!

YEAH. IT SEEMS I OWE YOU MY WHOLE WORLD.

REALLY? IN THAT CASE...

TWANG

THNK

BS·253

...WOULD YOU MIND RUNNING THIS PLATE FOR ME?

IS THERE A REASON YOU ASKED TO MEET ON THE ROOF?

SOME OF YOUR COLLEAGUES HAVE MIXED FEELINGS ABOUT ME. SOME HAVE VERY *CLEAR* FEELINGS ABOUT ME.

FEELINGS THEY'VE SHARED VERY LOUDLY, AND WITH MUCH PROFANITY, IN PUBLIC.

I RAN THE PLATE. IT WAS ISSUED IN 1952.

AND IT WAS REGISTERED TO A PLACE THAT'S BEEN ABANDONED FOR DECADES.

HMMM. SO, WE'RE TALKING TIME-TRAVELERS... OR...?

HERE. I WROTE THE ADDRESS ON THE BACK OF MY CARD. IF YOU NEED ANYTHING, DON'T HESITATE TO CALL.

SERIOUSLY? THANKS, DETECTIVE.

THANK YOU FOR SAVING MY WORLD.

ARE YOU PUTTING MY CARD IN YOUR PANTS?

I...I DON'T HAVE POCKETS.

THIS IS ACTUALLY A LONG-RUNNING ISSUE.

SO...WHAT? YOU'RE JUST GOING TO CARRY MY CARD AROUND IN YOUR PANTS IN CASE OF EMERGENCIES?

...APPARENTLY.

BYE!

I NEED SPIDER-POCKETS.

Mother of Exiles: *Part Three*

SPIDER-MAN. YOU REALLY NEED POCKETS.

UM... MISTER THE HUMAN TORCH?

JOHNNY'S FINE.

I NEED TO USE THE BATHROOM.

OH. UM... HANG ON.

OKAY. THE COAST IS CLEAR.

LET'S MOVE.

GAH!

YOU'RE JOHNNY STORM.

YEAH?

ARE YOU HERE FOR ME?

WHAT? NO. I'M A FRIEND OF YOUR ROOMMATE'S.

I KNOW THIS MUST LOOK WEIRD.

A WOMAN DOWN THE HALL DROPPED OFF THESE KIDS. WE THINK THEY'RE IN TROUBLE. I SAID I'D LOOK AFTER...

WAIT. *SHOULD* I BE HERE FOR YOU?

NEVER MIND.

NO NEED TO EXPLAIN, MAN.

I'M JUST GONNA BACK SLOWLY INTO MY ROOM. AND STAY THERE.

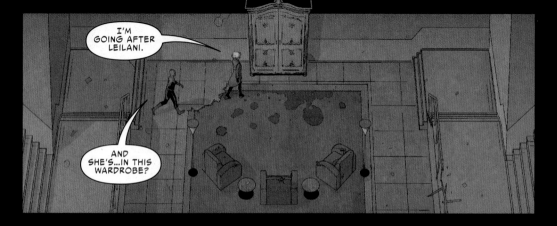

I'M GOING AFTER LEILANI.

AND SHE'S...IN THIS WARDROBE?

HAS SHE BEEN TAKEN TO NARNIA?

NO. WORSE, I'M AFRAID.

TAP TAP TAP

YOU GET BACK TO THE KIDS, PETER. KEEP THEM SAFE. I'LL BE BACK AS SOON AS I CAN.

tap TAP TAP

WHOA! YOU THINK I'M LETTING YOU DO... WHATEVER THIS IS ALONE?

YOU MAY KNOW MY REAL NAME, BUT YOU CLEARLY DON'T KNOW ME AT ALL.

I SAID I'D LOOK AFTER HER.

tap tap tap

FINE. WE'LL RESCUE HER TOGETHER.

PSSSHHH

I HAVE QUESTIONS.

THOUGHT YOU MIGHT.

WOW.

YOU SAID IT, MARNIE. NO. I MEANT THIS PLACE HAS GONE TO #@$%.

"THIS *WAS* A PARADISE."

"I GOT IN A WHOLE LOT OF FUN TROUBLE HERE BACK IN THE FORTIES."

"THE FORTIES? HOW OLD ARE YOU?"

"OLD ENOUGH TO FONDLY REMEMBER A TIME WHEN A MAN KNEW NOT TO ASK A WOMAN HER AGE."

"FOR A GENERATION, WE SHARED IDEAS IN SECRET WITH THE UNDER YORKERS. WE PROSPERED AS THEY DID."

"AND THEN?"

"THEY HAD A CHANGE IN LEADERSHIP."

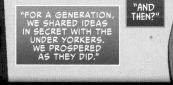

"THEY CLOSED THEMSELVES OFF. I GUESS THEY'VE HAD NO NEW BLOOD AND NO NEW IDEAS FOR SEVENTY YEARS. THEY'VE STAGNATED."

"LEILANI IS EITHER FROM HERE, OR IT'S POSSIBLE ONE OF THE RULING CLASS OF THIS PLACE WENT TOPSIDE AND MET HER."

"POOR GIRL."

BUT WHO AMONG US HASN'T HAD A MISGUIDED FLING WITH AN UNDERGROUND DESPOT?

ME. ME AMONG US HAS NOT HAD A MISGUIDED FLING WITH AN UNDERGROUND DESPOT.

OW.

WHY ARE THEIR FACES MADE OF SOLID PAIN?

HEY. LEILANI? PETER PARKER SENT ME. HE SAID YOU WERE AFTER A BETTER HERO, BUT I CAME ANYWAY.

IS PETER ALL RIGHT? THEY HIT HIM AND...

HE'S FINE. REALLY.

JASPER. TIERRA!

IT'S OKAY. THEY'RE BEING LOOKED AFTER. I PROMISE.

NOW, LET'S GET YOU OUT OF HERE AND--

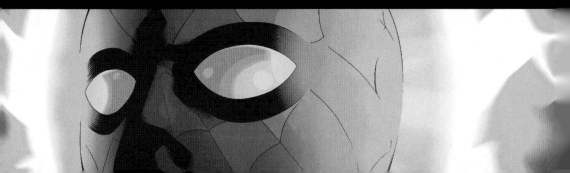

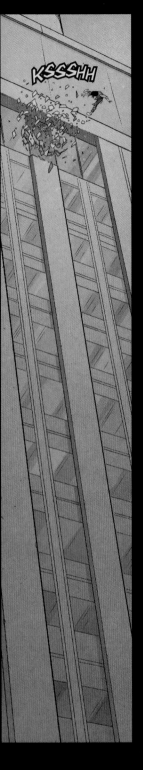

UNF!

GOING UP!

ARE YOU OKAY?

NOT REALLY. I WAS SHOT. WITH A BULLET.

WHEN I SAID I WANTED A VENT IN MY COSTUME, THIS ISN'T WHAT I MEANT.

RRRRR

WHAT'S HAPPENING?

WE'RE STOPPING.

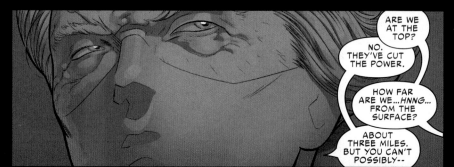

ARE WE AT THE TOP?

NO. THEY'VE CUT THE POWER.

HOW FAR ARE WE...HNNG... FROM THE SURFACE?

ABOUT THREE MILES. BUT YOU CAN'T POSSIBLY--

HNN.

THD

HNF.

I'LL CARRY HIM FROM HERE. HE'S EARNED A REST.

THAT WAS YOUR FATHER DOWN THERE?

RIGHT. WE'D BEST HURRY. HE'LL BE COMING TO THE SURFACE WITH AN ARMY AND AN APPALLING SENSE OF ENTITLEMENT.

YES.

WE SHOULD PROBABLY PREPARE FOR A SMALL WAR.

John Romita Sr. & **Frank D'Armata**
#1 Hidden Gem Variant

Mother of Exiles: *Part Four*

WHEN I WAS A KID, I LOST EVERYTHING.

MY AUNT AND UNCLE TOOK ME IN.

AND, OVER TIME, THEY MADE A SCARED KID FEEL SAFE AGAIN.

THEY LOOKED AFTER ME.

IT DIDN'T MATTER WHAT IT COST THEM.

THEY GAVE ME A HOME.

SOMEWHERE I BELONGED.

DID YOU BRING...?

PAINKILLERS AND BANDAGES. IN THAT ORDER. AS REQUESTED.

WHAT HAPPENED?

SPIDEY 009750 ✱X00 UNDER YORK TIME 631

INVADED AN UNDERGROUND CITY. TOOK ON AN EVIL RULER. RESCUED HIS DAUGHTER FROM THE TOP OF AN ALTERNATE EMPIRE STATE BUILDING SURROUNDED BY LAKES OF FIRE. YOU KNOW, THE USUAL.

HANG ON. DID YOU FREE A PRINCESS FROM A TOWER?

OH, HEY. DID WE?

OH.

NO.

ALSO, I WAS SHOT.

IT'S NOT MUCH OF A SHOT. HE'LL BE FINE.

AND... YOU ARE?

WE'LL DO THAT LATER. RIGHT NOW, AN ANGRY GROUP OF SUPER-STRONG UNDERGROUND PEOPLE ARE ABOUT TO ATTACK, AND THAT REALLY SHOULD BE OUR FOCUS.

CAN I BORROW YOUR PHONE AGAIN? I'LL CALL THE POLICE.

YEAH. BUT I HAVE SOMEONE ON MY SIDE THERE NOW.

THEY DIDN'T COME BEFORE.

SINCE... YESTERDAY?

I MAKE FRIENDS PRETTY QUICKLY.

HELLO?

HI. IS THIS DETECTIVE SEBBENS?

WHO'S ASKING?

UM. I GOT YOUR NUMBER FROM MY PANTS.

SPIDER-MAN?

YEAH. LOOK. THERE ARE SOME BAD PEOPLE COMING.

I DON'T KNOW HOW BIG IT'S GONNA GET, BUT I'M PRETTY SURE WE'LL NEED A WHOLE LOT OF POLICE.

WE'RE ON WATER STREET--

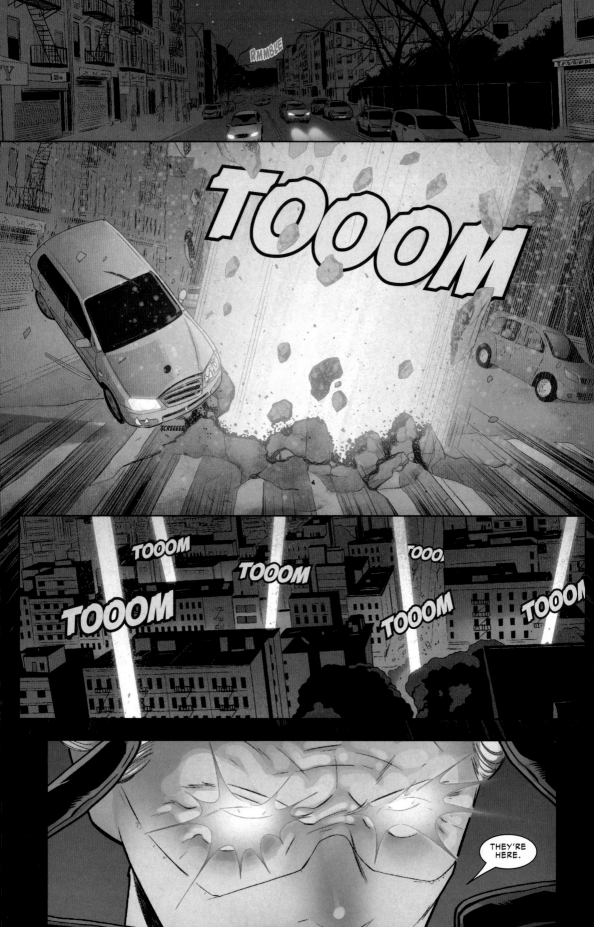

HUH?

no signal

...I UNDERSTAND.

CAPTAIN. AN ANONYMOUS TIP. AN ATTACK IS ABOUT TO OCCUR ON WATER STREET. I'D LIKE TO TAKE A FEW PATROLS DOWN AND--

DEET

WE HAVE ORDERS NOT TO GO INTO THAT LOCATION.

WHAT?

WHOSE ORDERS?

SO WE SERVE AND PROTECT...UNLESS SOMEONE TELLS US NOT TO?

HEY!

DETECTIVE!

CRNC

YOU WILL FEEL MY WRATH.

YOUR WRATH?

HRK!

LOOK. I REALIZE YOU LIVE IN THE PAST, BUT I'M NOT SURE I CAN BATTLE A VILLAIN WHO TALKS LIKE THAT. IT'S EMBARRASSING FOR BOTH OF US.

KOOOOOM

YOUR...YOUR WRATH FEELS A LOT LIKE PUNCHING.

RAAARGHH!

OKAY...

FOR THE RECORD, MIGUEL IS HOMELESS. BUT HERE HE IS, STANDING UP FOR OUR HOME.

SAME WITH GRACIE BESIDE HIM.

I RECOGNIZE THE SIX STUDENTS WHO LIVE IN A TWO-BEDROOM ACROSS THE ROAD. THERE'S A PARAMEDIC, A CHIROPRACTOR, A COUPLE OF TEACHERS, AND GARY, THE HOT DOG GUY.

ALONG WITH A BUNCH OF PEOPLE I DON'T KNOW.

ALL WILLING TO STAND UP FOR TOTAL STRANGERS.

THIS IS OUR HOME.

AND THAT'S OUR HERO, MAN. LET HIM GO.

DO YOU HAVE ANY IDEA WHO I--?

...THAT'S ENOUGH OF THAT.

NO.

NO ONE KNOWS WHO YOU ARE. NO ONE *CARES*. YOU'VE BEEN GONE TOO LONG. THEY'RE NOT IMPRESSED BY YOU. YOU CLOSED YOURSELF OFF AND NOW YOU'RE COMPLETELY IRRELEVANT.

NYPD. HANDS IN THE AIR!

I HAVE DIPLOMATIC IMMUNITY.

NOT SURE THAT COVERS WHATEVER THIS IS.

THAT WILL DO, OFFICER...

WE'RE ALL SO GRATEFUL TO THE MAYOR FOR STEPPING UP FOR HIS CITY!

IT'S TIME TO GO, HALE.

WHAT? WE HAVE AN ARRANGEMENT. I'M NOT GOING TO JUST--

WE WILL TALK LATER.

THAT'S IT. GO CRAWL BACK DOWN INTO THE PAST.

FISK...

LET'S NOT START A WAR YOU CAN'T POSSIBLY WIN.

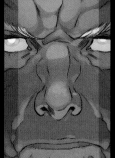

THNK

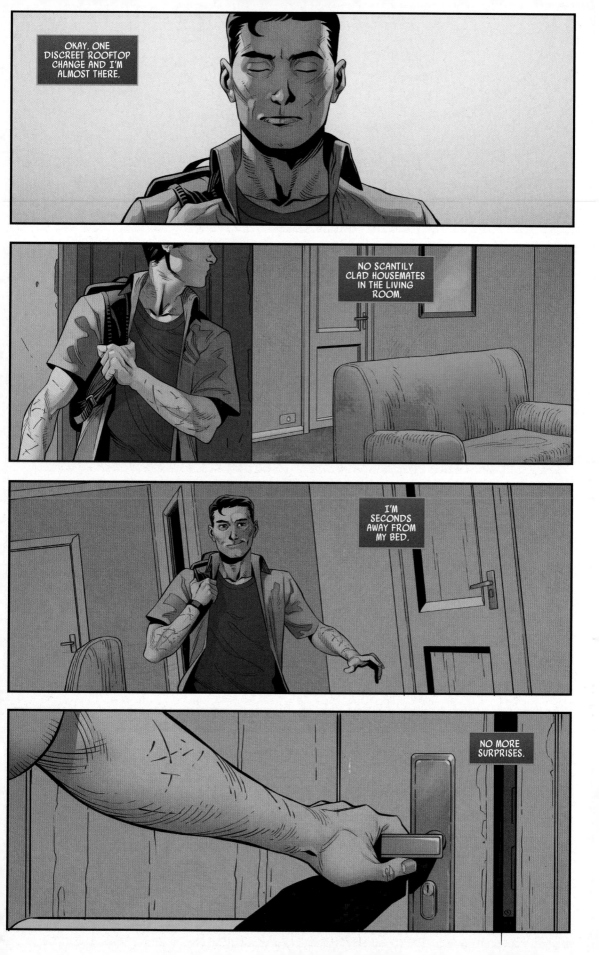

PETER.

AUNT MAY?

SORRY. I MISSED YOUR CALLS AND THEN...

ARE YOU ALL RIGHT?

I'M FINE. IT'S A LONG STORY.

AND IT'S A STORY I HAVEN'T HAD TIME TO MAKE UP YET.

IT INVOLVES A CAT.

PETER...

SOMETHING'S WRONG.

HAVE A SEAT, PLEASE.

MY HUMAN SENSE IS TINGLING.

I'M SORRY. THERE'S SOMETHING I NEED TO TELL YOU.

SOMETHING'S WRONG WITH AUNT MAY.

Juann Cabal & **Nolan Woodard**
#1 Variant

5

Not Running

...IN DANGER OF LOSING ONE OF THE MOST IMPORTANT PEOPLE IN MY LIFE.

THERE ARE PEOPLE YOU PUT ON A PEDESTAL, AND YOU NAIVELY EXPECT THEM TO STAY THERE.

MY FIRST ROUND OF CHEMOTHERAPY IS TOMORROW.

I KNOW MEN AND WOMEN WHO CAN LEVEL MOUNTAINS.

I'M FRIENDS WITH ACTUAL GODS.

I'VE SEEN THEM ALL KNOCKED DOWN.

BUT I'M JUST NOW REALIZING MAY HAS ALWAYS BEEN THE STRONGEST PERSON I KNOW.

I HATE TO ASK, BUT I WAS HOPING YOU COULD BE THERE TO...

I...HAVE A LOT GOING ON RIGHT NOW.

AND I HATE SEEING HER LIKE THIS.

VULNERABLE.

OF COURSE.

SCARED.

PETER.

AND HAVING TO BE BRAVE...

IT'S OKAY.

WE'LL GET THROUGH THIS.

...FOR ME.

"...SOME THINGS JUST HAVE TO BE FACED."

MAY PARKER?

YES.

I JUST NEED YOU TO FILL THESE OUT.

A NURSE WILL BE WITH YOU IN A MOMENT.

IS IT JUST YOU TODAY?

YES, DEAR.

RIGHT THIS WAY, MS. PARKER.

YOUR SON IS ALREADY WAITING.

MY SON...?

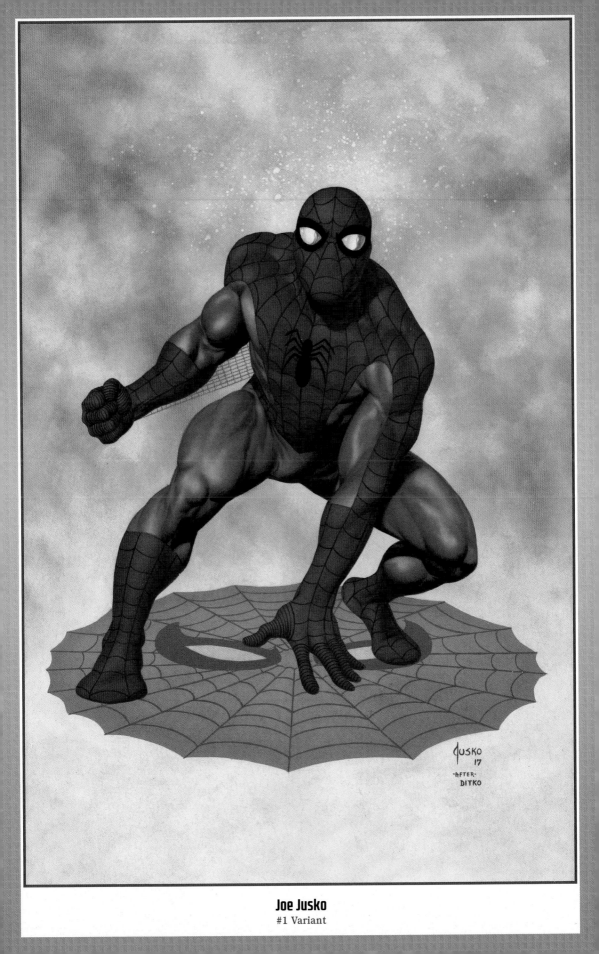

Joe Jusko
#1 Variant

6

Spider-Bite

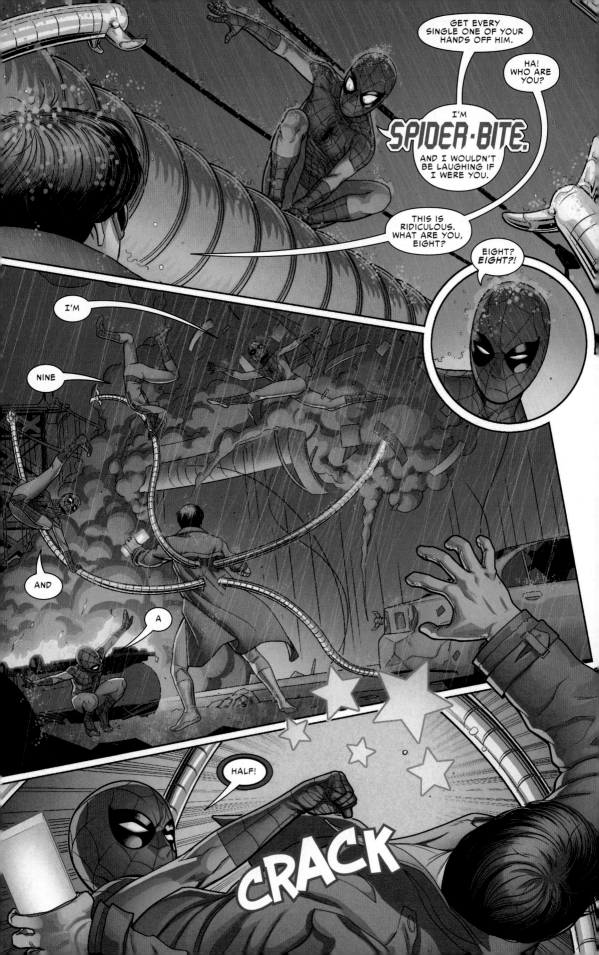

I DON'T KNOW HOW YOU PUT THIS TOGETHER, OSBORN!

ME? I'M NOT THE MASTERMIND BEHIND THIS.

THEN WHO...?

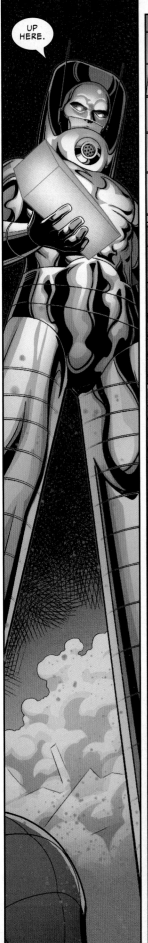

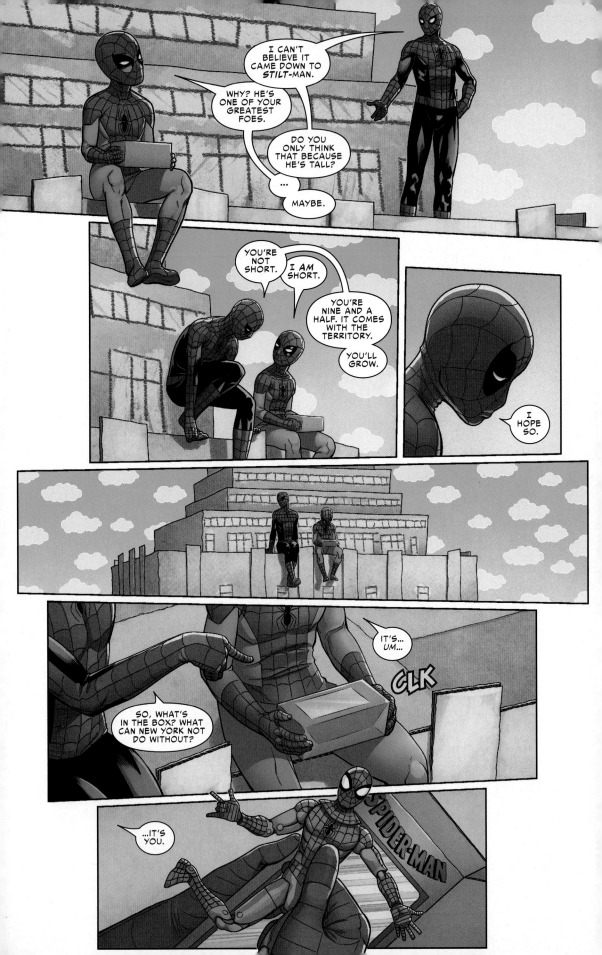

COME ON, NATHAN. TIME TO HOP DOWN.

STILT-MAN. YOU RIGHT WITH HIM?

I THINK I'LL MANAGE. THANK YOU.

YOU WERE A GREAT STILT-MAN, DAD.

THANKS. I'VE ALWAYS ASPIRED TO BE MORE FORMIDABLE BY BEING ABLE TO REACH THINGS ON HIGHER SHELVES.

HE... UH.

HE MAY HAVE BRUISED HIS ELBOW A BIT BETWEEN BATTLING DOC OCK AND SAVING THE CITY.

SMALL PRICE TO PAY.

THERE WERE A BUNCH OF CONTINUITY ERRORS AND PLOT HOLES, MOM, BUT I FOUGHT THE SINISTER SIXTY.

MY HERO.

NOW, I THINK IT'S TIME FOR BED.

I'M NOT TIRED.

COME ON. EVEN SUPER HEROES NEED REST. RIGHT, SPIDER-MAN?

ABSOLUTELY. SAVING THE WHOLE CITY IS EXHAUSTING.

I DON'T WANT TO GO TO BED!

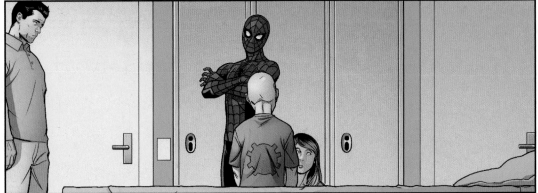

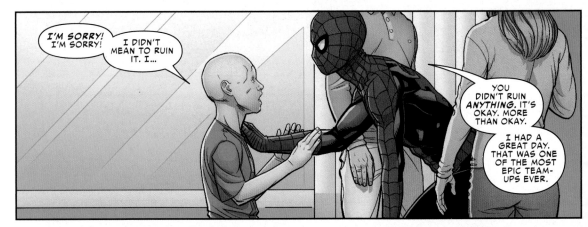

I'M SORRY! I'M SORRY! I DIDN'T MEAN TO RUIN IT. I...

YOU DIDN'T RUIN ANYTHING. IT'S OKAY. MORE THAN OKAY.

I HAD A GREAT DAY. THAT WAS ONE OF THE MOST EPIC TEAM-UPS EVER.

COULD WE HAVE A QUICK WORD?

SURE.

WILL YOU COME BACK? WILL YOU SAY GOODBYE?

OF COURSE. I'M NOT JUST GOING TO WALK AWAY FROM MY PARTNER.

Bryan Hitch & **David Curiel**
#2 Variant

Nao Fuji
#4 Marvel Meow Variant